MACMILLAN READERS

INTERMEDIATE LEVEL

RICHARD PRESCOTT

Ring of Thieves

MACMILLAN READERS

INTERMEDIATE LEVEL

Founding Editor: John Milne

The Macmillan Readers provide a choice of enjoyable reading materials for learners of English. The series is published at six levels – Starter, Beginner, Elementary, Pre-Intermediate, Intermediate and Upper.

Level control
Information, structure and vocabulary are controlled to suit the students' ability at each level.

The number of words at each level:

Starter	about 300 basic words
Beginner	about 600 basic words
Elementary	about 1100 basic words
Pre-Intermediate	about 1400 basic words
Intermediate	about 1600 basic words
Upper	about 2200 basic words

Vocabulary
Some difficult words and phrases in this book are important for understanding the story. Some of these words are explained in the story and some are shown in the pictures. From Pre-Intermediate level upwards, words are marked with a number like this: ...[3]. These words are explained in the Glossary at the end of the book.

Contents

The Places in This Story

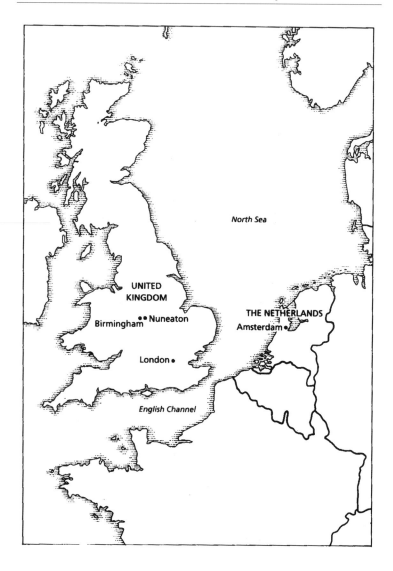

1

Who am I?

Something very strange was happening to me. My head hurt. I didn't know where I was. I couldn't remember my name. I couldn't remember anything.

My eyes were closed. I tried to think. Where was I? Who was I? Someone spoke to me.

'Are you all right?' a voice asked.

I opened my eyes. It was evening and almost dark. I was sitting on a long, wooden bench in a park. A teenage boy was standing in front of me. The boy had a dog with him. I couldn't see any other people. Everywhere was quiet.

'Are you all right?' the boy repeated. 'You look strange.'

I felt strange. I sat up straight. My whole body hurt. 'What happened to me?' I asked. 'Did I have an accident?'

'I don't know,' the boy said. 'I saw you walk here and sit down.'

'I walked here!' I said, surprised.

'Yes, can't you remember? It was about five minutes ago.'

I couldn't remember anything. The boy pointed behind me. 'You came from over there,' he said.

I turned and looked where the boy was pointing. I could see some trees. Beyond the trees, a train passed by slowly.

'What's over there?' I asked.

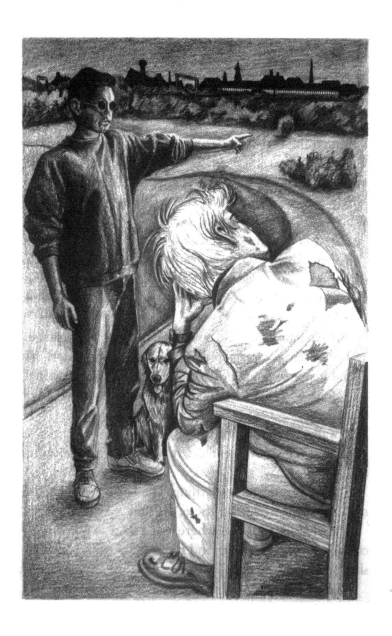

The boy pointed behind me.
'You came from over there,' he said.

'There's only the railway line,' the boy replied. 'But that's where you came from.'

'What place is this?' I asked.

The boy laughed. 'What do you mean?' he said. 'Don't you know?'

I didn't know.

'This is Nuneaton,' the boy said. He laughed again.

I repeated the name of the town to myself. The boy stood looking at me. My clothes were dirty. My jacket was torn[1].

'He thinks I'm mad,' I thought.

The boy moved away a little. 'Did someone attack[2] you?' he said. 'Have you been robbed?'

I put my hands in my pockets and checked quickly. In one pocket, I found my wallet. Some money was inside it and there were a few papers. In another pocket, I found a house key and a gold earring.

'Perhaps I've been robbed,' I said. 'But there's money in my wallet.'

'Shall I call the police?'

I didn't want to talk to the police. I wanted to go home. I needed a hot bath, an aspirin[3] and a long sleep.

'There's no need to call them,' I said. 'I'll report[4] the attack to the police tomorrow.'

'OK,' the boy said.

I thanked the boy for his help. Then I watched him and his dog walk away. I sat quietly for a few minutes. Slowly, I began to feel better. I tried hard to remember. But I could remember nothing. I had lost my memory.

should open

I had to find out my name and address. I checked my pockets again. The house key was important, of course. But where was the house? Luckily, I had my wallet. Perhaps the papers inside it could help me. I opened my wallet and took out the papers. On one of the pieces of paper was a note. It said: *Phone Harvey Chapman about appointment.* But there was no phone number.

I also found a train ticket. It was a return ticket[5] from Birmingham to London. The date on the ticket was 6th June. I checked the date on my watch. The dates were the same. I had been to London today. And I had left Birmingham this morning. But I wasn't in Birmingham now. I was in Nuneaton, a town near Birmingham.

There was a little pocket inside the wallet. In here, I found something very important – business cards. All the business cards were the same. They showed a name – my name – and a business and a home address:

JAMES KEATING

HOME: WORK:

12 SUTTON STREET   301 BELLOWS LANE
BIRMINGHAM   BIRMINGHAM
PHONE: PHONE
0121 2339509   0121 2364351

Part of the mystery was solved. I began to feel a little better. Now I could go home and rest. I walked across the park and into the town. I soon found the railway station. Birmingham wasn't far away. A train was leaving for Birmingham in fifteen minutes. I phoned the home phone number on my business card. Nobody answered. An answering machine[6] was connected to the phone. I left a message.

'This is James,' I said. 'I'm coming home.'

2

A Visitor in the Night

I sat on the train going to Birmingham and thought about what had happened. Part of the mystery was solved. But I couldn't explain a lot of things. For example, how had I arrived in Nuneaton? This town was near Birmingham. But it wasn't on a main railway line[7]. Trains going from London to Birmingham didn't go through there. This was part of the mystery without an answer. And there was another strange thing too – the earring.

I took it out of my pocket. The earring was dirty. It had dark stains on it. I touched my ears. There were no holes in them. The earring couldn't be mine. But whose was it? And why was it in my pocket?

By 10.30 I had arrived in Birmingham and a taxi had taken me to my house in Sutton Street. There were no lights on in the house. The house key from my pocket fitted the lock. I went inside and switched on the lights.

'Hello!' I shouted. 'This is James. I'm home!'

There was no answer. I opened all the doors and looked around the house. I checked the cupboards and drawers. There were only men's things. One person lived in this house. I lived alone.

The phone was in the living room. I listened to the messages on the answering machine. The last message was my own. I had left it when I phoned from the station. There were two other messages. One of them was from a woman. She sounded very angry.

'Where are you?' her voice said. 'You're always late. I'm always having to wait for you. You're terrible!' The woman didn't give her name.

The other message was from Harvey Chapman. His name was on one of the pieces of paper I had found in my pocket. He was angry too.

'I don't like the way you work, Keating,' his message began. 'You can't do business with Harvey Chapman like this! I hope you've got a good excuse[8] this time!'

Things were getting difficult for me. Two people were angry with me and I couldn't understand why.

There was nothing I could do now. I swallowed two aspirins and went upstairs to bed. My whole body hurt and I needed a long, long sleep.

'Tomorrow morning everything will be all right,' I said to myself. 'Tomorrow morning I'm sure I'll remember everything.'

I was too tired to wash. I got into bed and switched off the light. I fell asleep immediately.

Some time later, a noise woke me. Someone was coming up the stairs. I got out of bed and stood by the door. I didn't switch on the light.

'Burglars[9] are in the house,' I thought.

I got ready for a fight.

Suddenly the door opened and someone came in. I jumped and tried to grab[10] the person's neck. Immediately I was thrown into the air. I landed heavily on the floor.

The light came on. A woman was looking down at me.

She had long dark hair.

'What's happening?' I said. 'Who are you?'

'James!' the woman said. 'What's the matter with you? It's Susan.'

'Susan,' I repeated slowly. I looked at her. She had beautiful eyes. I knew that name. I knew those eyes. Yes, I remembered Susan.

'Yes, Susan,' she said. 'Your girlfriend. James, what is the matter with you?'

'I thought you were a burglar,' I said slowly.

Susan looked at me carefully. 'Are you all right?' she asked.

'Yes, I think so.'

'You've got bruises and cuts on your face. What has happened to you?'

'I don't know,' I said. 'I had an accident, or I was attacked. Perhaps both. I'm not sure. I've lost my memory – I can't remember anything.'

'Let's go downstairs. I'll make some tea,' Susan said. 'We can talk. I can help you remember.'

We talked in the kitchen while Susan made the tea. I told her what I could remember about the evening. Then we took our tea and sat on the couch[ll] in the living room. Susan helped me remember a lot of important things. This is what I learnt: I was thirty-two years old. I worked as a jeweller. I didn't have a jewellery shop. I made jewellery. I had a small workshop in Birmingham.

I asked Susan about yesterday and today. But she didn't know very much. She couldn't help me remember the last

'What's happening?' I said. 'Who are you?'

few days.

'I knew you were going to London,' Susan said. 'You had some business there.'

'Who did I meet?' I asked. 'Do you know?'

Susan shook her head. 'You didn't tell me. I expected you back in Birmingham at about 7.30. We were going to have dinner together. I phoned you at home, but you weren't there.'

'I heard your message on the answering machine,' I said. 'You were very angry.'

Susan smiled. 'I know. I thought you'd forgotten about the dinner. You often forget appointments.'

'I'm sorry, Susan,' I said. 'I can't remember arranging to have dinner with you.'

Susan came close to me and kissed me. 'Don't worry,' she said. 'After I left the message I became worried. I wasn't angry any more. I came to your house. I was worried about you. I wanted to speak to you. I decided to wait for you here. But then ...'

'Then I attacked you!'

'Yes, and I threw you to the floor!'

'You threw me very easily,' I said. 'How did you do it?'

'I've had a lot of practice,' Susan said. 'I'm a teacher of physical education and a judo champion[12]. Have you forgotten?'

I laughed. Of course, I had forgotten.

Susan laughed too. Then she said, 'Why were you in Nuneaton?'

'I don't know. Nuneaton isn't on the main railway line

between Birmingham and London.'

'Perhaps you got on the wrong train,' said Susan.

'Perhaps I didn't take the train at all,' I said.

I couldn't explain a lot of things. There was the gold earring. That was very strange too. My jacket was lying on a chair. I picked it up. I took the earring out of the pocket and showed it to Susan.

'I haven't got holes in my ears,' I said. 'The earring isn't mine.'

Susan looked at the earring carefully. 'What's this stain?' she said.

I looked at the stain. 'It's dirt,' I replied.

'It's not dirt,' Susan said. 'It's blood. This earring must belong to your attacker. Perhaps you had a fight. Perhaps you pulled the earring from your attacker's ear. That's your attacker's blood on the earring.'

Susan stopped talking for a moment. We drank some of our tea. It tasted good.

'What business were you doing in London?' she asked. She was worried now.

'I don't know,' I replied. 'That's the problem. I can't remember anything about being in London.'

'Your "accident" in Nuneaton may be connected with[13] the business in London. There are a few questions we must answer. Who did you see in London? What was the business about? Did you take the train from London to Nuneaton? Or did somebody take you to Nuneaton? Who did you have a fight with?'

'I'm doing business with a man called Harvey

15

Chapman,' I said. 'Perhaps he has something to do with my accident.'

'Harvey Chapman!' Susan said, surprised.

'Who is he? Do you know him?'

'Harvey Chapman is an actor. He's married to the Hollywood film star, Pauline Greenwood. Are you making jewellery for Chapman?'

'Well, I think so,' I said slowly. 'He's very angry with me. I'm not sure why. He left a message on my answering machine this evening. Perhaps I met Harvey Chapman in London.'

'I don't think so,' Susan said. 'Harvey Chapman lives in Los Angeles most of the time. But he's not American, he's English. He was born in Birmingham. When he comes to England, he always stays at his house here.'

I finished my tea and sat back on the couch. I closed my eyes. I didn't want to think about Harvey Chapman now. I felt very, very tired.

'You need to rest,' Susan said. 'Go back to bed. I can come and see you tomorrow morning. I don't have to go to work. It is the school holidays. I'm sure you'll be feeling better in the morning. Perhaps you'll be able to remember something about today. I hope so.'

I hoped so too. We said goodnight and I went to bed. The clock beside my bed showed 12.30. I was very tired, but happy to be home. I was happy, too, about Susan. I lay for a short time and thought about her. Yes, I remembered Susan. She was wonderful.

3

Money Problems

I woke early, about seven o'clock. I had slept very well. My head didn't hurt. I felt much better. I lay in bed, thinking. Some of my memory had returned. I was pleased about that. But I remembered nothing about my visit to London or my "accident".

Susan arrived while I was eating breakfast. We had some coffee together. Then, at about nine o'clock we went to the police station. Susan drove us in her car.

I told my story and a young police-officer wrote down the details. This didn't take very long. There wasn't much to say.

'I think I was attacked,' I said. 'But I don't think anything was stolen.'

'Can you describe your attacker?' the police-officer asked.

'I'm sorry, I can't,' I replied. 'But I can tell you something about him.'

'Or her,' Susan said.

I remembered the strength of Susan's judo throw. 'Or her,' I said. 'Perhaps my attacker was a woman. Anyway, she or he has one ear that is hurt.'

I showed the earring to the police-officer. 'There's blood on the earring,' I said. 'I must have pulled the earring from my attacker's ear.'

'We'll keep this earring,' the police-officer said. 'It may

be useful.' He put it in a plastic bag.

I signed my report and then we left the police station. Next, we drove to my workshop. The workshop was in an old part of the city. There were a lot of jewellery workshops here. Some of them were big. Others were small. Mine was very small. It was on the first floor of a dirty old building. A factory was on the ground floor. A narrow, dark, wooden staircase went up to the first floor. I had two rooms at the top of the stairs. I had a little office and a door at the back led to another small room – my workshop. All my tools were here. This was where I made all my jewellery.

Susan and I looked around the office. It wasn't very tidy[14].

'Where's your appointments book?' Susan asked. 'We must find it. Then we can check your appointments for yesterday.'

We looked everywhere but we couldn't find my appointments book. There were pieces of paper lying on a

*We looked everywhere but we couldn't
find my appointments book.*

table, chairs, a desk and on top of the cupboards. Some of the papers had appointments and phone numbers written on them.

Susan became very angry. 'You're terrible,' she said. 'You're so untidy! It's impossible to find anything here!'

Susan was right. The office was in a mess. I am a very untidy person.

After about ten minutes, Susan found my appointments book. It was at the back of a drawer in my desk. She opened the book and she was silent for a few moments.

'What's the matter?' I said.

She didn't answer. She gave the book to me. I looked inside. Most of the pages were empty. I didn't often write appointments in it.

'Don't be angry, Susan,' I said. 'I know I'm untidy. I write most of my appointments on pieces of paper.'

Susan looked around the room. There were pieces of paper everywhere. 'Then you lose your pieces of paper,' she said. 'And you forget your appointments. You're terrible! Now we'll never know why you went to London.'

We began to tidy the office. We put all the notes and phone numbers together. We tidied the desk drawers and the cupboards. In one cupboard I found a lot of drawings. The drawings were designs for jewellery. Most of the designs were for simple, inexpensive[15] jewellery. Two other designs were very different. These designs interested me. They were unusual. They weren't simple. And the stones in the designs were going to be diamonds.

One of the designs was for a brooch[16]. The drawing

showed a large diamond in the centre of the brooch with some smaller diamonds around it. The other design was for a ring. This had two medium-sized diamonds in it.

On the design of the brooch there was a note in my handwriting. The note said: *The diamonds must be pure and transparent*[17]. Pure, transparent diamonds are the best quality. They are very, very expensive.

In one corner of the drawing I had written Harvey Chapman's name, address and phone number.

Harvey Chapman must be an important customer. Perhaps the brooch and the ring were for Pauline Greenwood, the film star. I showed the designs to Susan.

'One day Pauline Greenwood will wear my jewellery,' I said. 'That'll be fantastic, won't it?'

'Oh, yes,' replied Susan. 'She's very famous. If she wears your jewellery, perhaps you'll be famous too.'

Suddenly, the phone rang. I answered it. An angry voice shouted in my ear.

'This is Harvey Chapman. Now listen to me, Keating, I made three appointments with you last week. You didn't come to any of them! I'm tired of this[18]. Do you understand? Where were you yesterday evening?'

I remembered my note. *Phone Harvey Chapman about appointment*, it had said.

'I wanted to phone you, Mr Chapman,' I said. 'I'm very sorry, but I had an accident.'

'I don't want to hear about any accidents,' said Harvey Chapman angrily. 'I want to see you. And I want to see you today!'

21

'What do you want to see me about?' I asked.

'Are you trying to be funny?' Chapman said.

'No, I'm sorry,' I said. 'You see I had an accident. I lost my memory and ...'

'Keating, I'm not stupid,' Chapman said. 'Don't lie to me. Now listen, I have to see you. I want to change the design of the jewellery. Can you come to my house this morning?'

I was going to be busy today. I didn't want to see Harvey Chapman this morning.

'What about this evening?' I said. 'I'll come at seven o'clock.'

'OK, but don't be late,' Chapman said. 'And don't forget to come this time.' He put the phone down.

I wrote on a piece of paper: *Harvey Chapman – seven o'clock.* I put the paper in my pocket.

One of the things I had to do was to go to the bank. I needed some money. Susan stayed at the workshop. She wanted to finish tidying up. We agreed to meet later.

At the bank, I had a very unpleasant surprise.

'I'm sorry, Mr Keating,' the bank clerk[19] told me. 'You can't take any money from your account.'

'Why not?' I asked.

'There is no money in your account,' the clerk said.

'But that's impossible! This must be a mistake.'

I asked to see the manager. The manager took me into her office.

'You took out twenty thousand pounds from your account yesterday,' the manager explained.

'How is that possible?' I asked. 'I was in London yesterday.'

'I know. You took the money from a London branch of the bank.'

'I can't understand it.'

'You had some business in London,' the manager said. 'You went to our branch in Baker Street. You asked to take out twenty thousand pounds from your account. The manager there phoned me. I spoke to him and then I spoke to you. Everything was done in the correct way. Surely you remember?'

'I'm afraid I can't remember. That's the problem,' I said. 'Something strange happened yesterday. I had an accident. And I've lost my memory of what happened yesterday.'

'I'm sorry,' the bank manager said. 'Can I help in any way?'

'Perhaps you can,' I said. 'I know I had business in London. But why did I need twenty thousand pounds?'

'I can tell you that,' the manager said. 'You told me when we spoke on the phone. You were going to buy diamonds. I'm afraid that's all I know.'

I thanked the manager and left the bank. Twenty thousand pounds is a lot of money. The diamonds must have been very special ones. It was possible that I had bought the diamonds to make Harvey Chapman's brooch and ring. Slowly things were becoming clearer. I had been attacked. I knew this much. But my problems were getting worse. Had the diamonds been stolen? Had the money been stolen? And there were other questions. Where was I attacked? How did I get to Nuneaton?

It was 10.30. I decided to go immediately to London. I wanted to speak to the people at the branch of the bank in Baker Street. Perhaps they could tell me something. Perhaps I had gone to the bank with someone. I had to find out as much as possible about that day in London. The bank in Baker Street was the best place to start finding answers to my questions.

4

The Chilton Hotel

I phoned Susan immediately. I told her that I was going to London.

'You're not going on your own,' she told me. 'I don't want you to have another accident. I'm coming too.'

Susan was right. It was better not to go alone. 'OK,' I said. 'Meet me at the station as soon as you can.'

About twenty minutes later, Susan had bought our tickets and we were on the train to London. On the journey, I told Susan about the twenty thousand pounds and the diamonds.

Susan wasn't pleased. 'Why did you want to pay for the diamonds in cash[20]?' she said. 'Isn't it safer to pay by cheque[21]? Or can't your bank pay the money into the account of the diamond dealer[22]? You don't need to use cash, do you?'

'I don't often buy expensive diamonds,' I explained. 'And when I do I don't usually pay for them in cash. But sometimes cash is better than a cheque.'

'I don't understand,' said Susan.

'If you pay in cash, you can often get a better deal[23]— you pay a lot less,' I explained.

Susan shook her head. 'I don't like you doing that, James. It's very stupid to pay in cash. Twenty thousand pounds is a lot of money. Now the diamonds have been stolen. There is no record of the sale. You have lost everything. And it's all your own fault[24]. You really have been very stupid, James.'

I felt very stupid. But that didn't help me. Susan and I didn't speak for the rest of the journey. We didn't speak again until we arrived in London at 12.20.

We took a taxi from Euston Station and went straight to the bank in Baker Street. Susan paid the driver.

The bank was quite busy. I asked to see the manager. A clerk told us to wait for a moment. While we were waiting, I looked around the bank. I had been here yesterday. But I could remember nothing about my visit. Five bank clerks were serving customers.

'One of those clerks must have served me yesterday,' I thought.

At last, the manager said he could speak with us. We sat down in his office and I introduced myself.

'I'm James Keating . . .'

'Yes, Mr Keating,' the manager said, 'I remember you from yesterday.'

He remembered me! This was a good start. I began to feel happier.

'What can I do for you?' the manager said, smiling.

I explained my problem. The manager listened carefully.

'I'm very sorry,' the manager said, when I had finished speaking.

'You see,' I went on, 'it's very important for me to find out as much as possible about yesterday. Where did I go? Who did I see?'

The manager spoke into the phone on his desk.

'Ask Martin Sanders to come in here for a moment, please,' he said. Then the manager looked up and said to me, 'It was about 1.30 yesterday when you came to see me. We phoned the manager of your bank in Birmingham. We made the arrangements. Then one of our clerks here gave you the money. You didn't tell me where you were going with the money.'

There was a knock on the door and a young man came in. 'Ah, Martin,' the manager said. 'You remember Mr Keating from yesterday, don't you? He took out twenty thousand pounds from his account. You gave him the money.'

'That's right,' Sanders said.

The manager went onto explain my problem. 'Perhaps you can help, Martin. Where did Mr Keating go after he left the bank? Did he tell you? Or did you see where he went?'

Martin Sanders shook his head. 'I don't know where he went *after* he left the bank,' he said slowly. Then he continued, 'But I do know where he was before he came here.'

This was interesting. I sat up straight in my chair. 'Anything you know may be useful to me,' I said. 'Where did you see me?'

'I was walking back to the bank after my lunch. It was almost 1.30. There were a lot of people in the street. Suddenly, someone ran into me. It was you, Mr Keating. You were in a hurry. You had come out of the Chilton Hotel. Later, I saw you again in the bank, when you came

'Suddenly, someone ran into me.
It was you, Mr Keating.'

out of this office.'

'That's very interesting, Mr Sanders,' I said. 'You've been a great help. Thank you very much.'

Martin Sanders smiled.

'And by the way,' I said, 'I'm sorry that I ran into you.'

Sanders smiled again. 'That's all right,' he said.

I must have met someone at the Chilton Hotel. Perhaps I had seen the diamonds there. Then I had gone to the bank to get the twenty thousand pounds. I had returned to the hotel and paid for the diamonds. There couldn't be another explanation. But who had I met at the hotel? That was the most important question to answer now.

5

Karen Winter

The Chilton Hotel wasn't far from the bank. We walked there. It was a fine old building.

There was a porch over the pavement outside. A doorman in uniform stood outside. We went under the porch and entered the hotel. The doorman said good afternoon as we walked in.

A young woman sat at the reception desk. She was well-dressed and friendly. She looked up and smiled.

'Good afternoon, can I help you?' she said.

I told my story again. I explained about my accident and about my loss of memory. I didn't say anything about the diamonds.

'I think I came here to meet someone,' I said. 'Do you remember seeing me?'

'Yes, I do,' the receptionist replied. 'I saw you arrive at about 12.30.'

'Who did I meet? Can you tell me that?'

'You came here to meet a woman,' the receptionist said.

'A woman?' I said.

'Yes, I think she was Dutch,' the receptionist said.

'What was her name?'

'Wait a moment,' she said. 'I'll check our computer records for you.' She typed something on the computer keyboard in front of her. She looked at the computer screen. 'Karen Winter,' the receptionist said.

Karen Winter? I knew no one of that name. I couldn't remember meeting her.

'Did I leave the hotel at about 1.30 and then come back again?' I asked.

'Yes, you did.'

'And what time did I leave afterwards?'

'I'm not really sure,' she said. 'I think you left at about 2.30.'

'Can you tell me Karen Winter's address?'

'Hotel guests don't have to give us their addresses, sir,' she said.

'Haven't you got any details about her on the computer?' I asked.

She looked at the computer screen. 'The room was booked[25] for one night. The booking was made by AT Travel, a travel company in Amsterdam. Karen Winter checked into the hotel at 8.30 p.m. on 5th June. She checked out at 3.15 the next day. She paid in cash. That's all the information I have, sir.'

It was now after two o'clock. Susan and I hadn't eaten since breakfast and we were hungry. We left the hotel and went to a pub. We ordered sandwiches and drinks. We sat down to eat and talk.

It had been an interesting day. We had discovered some important facts. But there were still many questions to answer. What did I do after leaving the Chilton Hotel? Did I go straight back to the railway station? Or did I meet some other people? How did I get to Nuneaton?

It was important to contact Karen Winter. Perhaps she could help me answer these questions. I needed to speak to Karen Winter for other reasons as well. The diamonds had probably[26] been stolen in Nuneaton when I was attacked. I wanted to get the diamonds back again. But what kind of diamonds did I buy? How many were there? Only Karen Winter could tell me. I had to find her. But how? It wasn't going to be easy.

'Can't you remember anything about Karen Winter, James?' Susan asked. 'What did she look like, for example?'

I tried to remember. I drank some of my drink and closed my eyes. At last, I thought I could remember something.

After a few moments I said, 'I think she had long blonde hair. She was about thirty-five years old. She wore glasses.'

'Are you sure?' Susan asked.

'I'm sure. Very sure.'

We finished our drinks and sandwiches. I looked at my watch. It was almost three o'clock. 'Come on, let's go,' I said. 'There's nothing more we can do in London.'

We left the pub. As we walked along the street, we passed the Chilton Hotel. The doorman was still standing outside.

'Just a moment,' Susan said to me. 'There are a few more questions I'd like to ask the receptionist.'

The receptionist looked up and smiled as we walked in.

'I'm sorry. But I have another question,' Susan said. 'It's about Karen Winter.'

'Yes?'

'You told us she left the hotel yesterday afternoon. Where did she go? Do you know?'

'She asked me to phone for a taxi,' the receptionist said. 'The taxi took her to the airport.'

'So she was probably going back to Holland,' Susan said.

'Yes, I expect so,' the receptionist said.

We thanked the receptionist and turned to leave. As we were going out Susan said, 'Oh – what does Karen Winter look like?'

'She's about forty years old with short, dark hair.'

'Does she wear glasses?' Susan asked.

'No, I didn't see her wearing glasses.'

'Thanks again,' Susan said.

When we were outside Susan began to laugh.

'What's so funny?' I asked.

'It's you, James,' Susan said, laughing. She held my hand and kissed me. 'You're terrible. You were never good at remembering things. Your description of Karen Winter was totally wrong!'

I didn't reply. My memory was terrible. I began laughing as well.

We went straight to Euston Station and caught the train to Birmingham. On the train we talked about Karen Winter.

'There's one thing I don't understand,' Susan said. 'How did Karen Winter contact you first? Where and when did you first speak to her? Can't you remember?'

I didn't answer. I looked at her.

Susan laughed. 'Oh, sorry, of course you can't,' she said.

'Let's think about this,' I said. 'Where have I been recently? Have I been to Holland, for example?'

'That's it!' Susan said. 'Why didn't I think of it before? About a month ago, you went to a jewellery trade fair[27] in Amsterdam. You probably met Karen Winter there.'

'OK,' I said. 'We'll have to look through my papers in Birmingham. I probably brought home some leaflets and brochures from the trade fair. I'm sure there'll be some business cards as well. Karen Winter's business card will be among them.'

'Yes,' said Susan. 'When I was tidying your office this morning I saw a lot of leaflets and brochures. We'll have to look through them carefully.'

Everything was going well. I began to feel happier. I was sure that we could find Karen Winter. She would be able to help me. She could describe the diamonds to me. She could tell me how many diamonds I had bought. Then I could talk to the police again. I might get the diamonds back again!

Some time later the train stopped at Nuneaton Station. This was interesting. We hadn't gone through Nuneaton in the morning. Why was the train stopping at Nuneaton now?

The train started moving again and left Nuneaton behind. Outside the station there was a sharp bend[28] in the railway line and the train had to slow down. On the left of the line there was an enormous park. Suddenly I understood. This was where I had fallen from the train. This was where I had my accident. I looked at Susan. She understood too.

'So I did come back from London by train,' I said. 'And it was here that I had my accident. It was here that I fell out of the train.'

'Or you were pushed out of the train,' Susan said. 'Remember the earring with blood stains on it? Perhaps there was a fight and you were pushed out of the train.'

Before we got to Birmingham, a ticket inspector came to check our tickets.

'Express trains[29] don't usually go through Nuneaton, do they?' I asked the ticket inspector.

'You're right, sir,' the ticket inspector said. 'Workmen are repairing the main railway line. That's why the trains are all going through Nuneaton.'

'But we didn't go through Nuneaton this morning,' I said.

'You're right again, sir,' he said. 'The line going south is OK. Only the line going north is being repaired.'

So now the mystery of my day in London had been solved. I had met Karen Winter in the Chilton Hotel. I had paid her twenty thousand pounds in cash for some diamonds. She had left for Holland. I had come back to Birmingham by train. Then, when the train was near Nuneaton Station, I had been attacked and the diamonds had been stolen. Then my attackers had thrown me out of the train.

Suddenly I understood. This was where
I had fallen from the train.

6

An Angry Customer

It was almost seven o'clock when we arrived in Birmingham. It was a warm evening. The shops had closed. The streets of the city were quiet. We were hungry so we decided to have some dinner. We would go back to my office and look for Karen Winter's business card later.

Susan had left her car in a car park near the station. We walked to the car park and drove to Susan's flat. She lived in a quiet area not far from the city centre. Her flat was on the second floor of a large old house. There was a beautiful garden all round the house. Susan's flat looked down on to the garden at the back.

Susan opened the windows. The warm summer air came into the room. There was a pleasant smell of flowers.

'OK, you get some drinks,' Susan said. 'And I'll start getting dinner ready. You'll find some cold drinks in the fridge. I'll have a glass of fruit juice.'

That's what I liked about Susan. She was always so well-organized[30].

After dinner we drove to my office. Susan parked the car outside. As I put my hand in my jacket pocket for the keys to my workshop, I found a piece of paper. I gave the keys to Susan and looked at the paper. There was a note on it, which said: *Harvey Chapman – seven o'clock.*

I looked at my watch. It was 9.15.

'Oh, no,' I said. 'I've done it again!'

'Done what?' asked Susan.

'I've forgotten about Harvey Chapman! I had an appointment with him at seven o'clock this evening. He'll kill me.'

I unlocked the door and climbed the narrow, wooden staircase and went into my office. I phoned Harvey Chapman immediately. I thought he would be angry. He was. He shouted so loudly that my ear hurt. He said some very unpleasant things. I waited for him to stop shouting.

'I'm very sorry, Mr Chapman,' I said. 'I understand how you feel. Look, I'll come and see you immediately. I'll be at your house in twenty minutes.'

I put the phone down before he could start shouting again.

'I've got to go and see Chapman,' I told Susan. 'You stay here. Look through all the information about the Amsterdam trade fair. You may be lucky and find Karen Winter's business card.'

'OK,' Susan said. She threw me the keys to her car. 'You'll need these,' she said.

'Thanks.'

'Oh, James.'

'Yes?'

'You won't forget to come back for me, will you?'

I smiled. Then I held her close to me and kissed her.

'I won't forget,' I said. 'I'll be back in a couple of hours. Good luck with your search.'

Susan looked around the room. There was still a lot of tidying up to do. 'I'll need good luck to find anything in this mess,' she said.

I opened the cupboard where I kept my jewellery designs. I took out the designs I had made for Harvey Chapman. There were two: one was of a brooch and the other was of a ring. *The diamonds must be pure and transparent*, my note said. What trouble those diamonds were giving me!

Harvey Chapman lived in a big house in a quiet part of town. Tall trees grew on both sides of the road. There was a red Ferrari sports car outside the house. I parked next to the Ferrari.

Harvey Chapman had heard me arrive. When I got out of the car he was standing at the front door. He was a tall, strong-looking man. He had fair hair and his skin was sun-tanned. He wore a brightly coloured shirt. He held a drink in his right hand.

'You're only two and a half hours late, Keating!' he said. 'But at least you're here this time.'

Chapman wasn't American, but he spoke with an American accent.

I followed Chapman into the house. He led me into a room at the back of the house. There were large windows which looked out onto the garden. Outside, in the garden, I could see a swimming pool.

It was beginning to get dark now. Harvey Chapman switched on the lights. He poured another drink into his glass. He didn't offer me a drink. We sat down at a table.

'Now let's get this clear[31],' Chapman said in a loud voice. 'Do you want to work for me or not?'

'Of course I do, Mr Chapman,' I said.

'Well,' Chapman went on. 'You're a good jeweller. I like your work. But I don't like you. I don't like you at all. I don't like the way you do business. You're lazy and you're dishonest. You're never here when I need you.'

Hearing Chapman say this made me angry. I tried not to show my anger. 'I've had a few problems recently,' I said.

'I don't want to hear about your problems,' Chapman replied. 'I want you to do a job for me. That's what I'm paying you for.'

I didn't reply. I put the jewellery designs on the table. 'You wanted to change the designs,' I said. 'What do you want to change?'

Chapman looked at the design of the brooch. He picked up a pencil and changed the drawing. He drew some leaves around the diamonds. 'I want these to be gold,' he said.

I didn't like the changes, but I said nothing. I took the pencil from Chapman and made his drawing better.

'Good,' Chapman said. 'That's good. I like it.'

'Now what about the ring?' I said. 'How do you want to change that?'

Chapman looked puzzled[32]. 'What ring?' he said.

I pointed to the design of the ring. 'This ring,' I said.

Chapman looked carefully at the design. The design showed a beautiful diamond ring. I was very pleased with it. It was one of the best designs I had made.

'Are you trying to be funny again?' Chapman said. 'I

never asked you to make a ring for me. What are you talking about?'

Now I was puzzled. If I wasn't making the ring for Chapman, who was I making it for? I didn't know.

'I'm sorry, Mr Chapman. I've made a mistake. I thought the ring was for you.' I picked up the design.

Chapman stopped me. 'No, wait a minute,' he said. 'It's a beautiful ring. I like it.' Chapman looked closely at the design. 'I like it very much. The brooch and the ring would look good together.'

I agreed with him. But I began to get worried. Who had asked me to make the ring? I must have another important customer. This customer must have a lot of money to spend and liked beautiful jewellery. But who was it? I couldn't remember.

'I'd like to buy the ring,' Chapman said. 'How much do you want for it?'

'I'm afraid I can't make it for you,' I told him.

'But you said a minute ago it was mine!'

'Yes, but I was wrong. You see, after my accident, I haven't been able to remember things very well.'

Chapman smiled. 'I don't know if you're very clever or very stupid,' he said. 'Anyway, you're a good salesman. I want the ring. How much? Tell me the price!'

Chapman hadn't understood. He didn't know I was telling him the truth. The design was specially made for another customer. How could I sell Chapman someone else's ring?

'No, I'm sorry,' I said. 'I've made a terrible mistake. I

can't make the ring for you.'

Now Chapman got angry. He stood up. 'What do you mean, Keating?' he shouted. 'You come here, show me the design of a ring. You ask me if I want to change it. And then you tell me I can't have it. Keating, I don't like the way you do business. But I want that ring. Now, if you won't say a price, I will. I'll give you ten thousand pounds. You can have five thousand pounds now. I'll give you another five thousand when the ring is finished. OK?'

I shook my head. 'No, Mr Chapman.'

Chapman banged his hand on the table. He was very angry. 'Listen Keating,' he shouted. 'Perhaps you are stupid after all. I'm an important customer for you. Don't you understand that? I have many rich friends in Hollywood. I know a lot of film stars. Wouldn't you like to see those film stars wearing your jewellery? Of course you would! Your name would be in all the best fashion magazines. I could make you famous, Keating. Can't you understand that?'

I understood it. Chapman was right. I also understood something else. I had big money problems. Some very valuable diamonds had been stolen.

I didn't like Chapman. But I needed him. I needed his rich friends. If I made jewellery for them, I would have money in the bank again. And of course, it would be nice to be a famous jewellery designer too. Yes, I needed Chapman.

'OK, Mr Chapman,' I said. 'I'll make you the ring.'

'Listen Keating,' he shouted. 'Perhaps you are stupid
after all. I'm an important customer for you.'

7

No Answer

Chapman and I arranged to meet again in a few days. He had to go back to America soon. He wanted to take the jewellery with him.

It was about 10.30 when I left Chapman's house. I felt unhappy as I drove back to my office. Chapman was an unpleasant man. I disliked him as much as he disliked me. But I had to work for him. I needed the money.

I climbed the narrow staircase to my office. I hoped Susan had found some answers. I went inside. Susan was sitting at the desk. The office was tidy. She smiled but said nothing. She handed me a couple of pieces of paper. One of them was a leaflet. It advertised jewellery. The leaflet came from the Amsterdam Jewellery Trade Fair. On the leaflet, I had written Karen Winter's name and phone number:

Karen Winter
De Wolf Diamonds
Amsterdam 674863

'De Wolf must be the name of the company she works for,' Susan said.

The other piece of paper was an old envelope. There was a note written on the back:

Winter, Chilton Hotel, 12.30
Best quality diamonds for Chapman

I kissed Susan. 'You're fantastic,' I said.

'And you're terrible!' she replied. 'It took me more than an hour to find those papers. The envelope was on the floor in your workshop. The leaflet was behind one of the cupboards. You must try to be tidier James.'

Susan drove me home to my house. She had things to do at her flat the next morning. So we arranged to meet for lunch at her flat the next day.

At midnight I went to bed. I slept until eight o'clock.

When I woke it was a bright sunny morning. After breakfast, I tried phoning Karen Winter in Amsterdam. The phone rang, but there was no answer. I would have to phone again later.

Today was going to be another busy day. I had to start work on Chapman's jewellery. I needed to buy some more diamonds. I would have to arrange a loan[33] from the bank for more diamonds. I hoped to buy the diamonds from Karen Winter.

There were a few other things to do as well. One of them was to find out about the ring. Who was I making it for? I wanted to check in my workshop. Perhaps I had written down some notes about the ring somewhere. I could check in my list of orders[34].

Before leaving my house to go to my office, I phoned Karen Winter's number again. Her phone rang for a long time. But there was still no answer.

I got to my office at nine o'clock. Now that my office was tidy, it was easier to find things. I had a file marked "New Orders". I looked through the file. There were a lot of orders from shops. Most of the orders were for repairs to old jewellery. But the list wasn't complete. For example, Chapman's name wasn't in the file. But I knew I had an order from him. I was looking for an order for a diamond ring. I couldn't find one. Who had ordered the ring? I tried to think, but I couldn't remember. All I could do now was wait. The customer would have to contact me.

I phoned Karen Winter again. Still no answer. I went into my workshop. There was a small safe[35] in one corner. This was where I kept my valuable materials – gold, silver, precious stones. I opened the safe and took out a long, thin piece of gold. I measured the gold and cut as much as I needed. Then I began work on Chapman's brooch.

I worked hard all morning. Several times, I phoned Karen Winter. Each time I got no answer. Why did no one answer? If the number was Karen Winter's office phone number, someone should answer the phone.

'Perhaps it's her home number,' I thought. 'That's why she isn't answering.' But I didn't really believe it. Why should Karen Winter give me her home phone number? There was one other possibility. Perhaps I had written the number down incorrectly. I'm an untidy person. Its possible that I had made a mistake when I wrote down the number. But I was sure I had spoken to Karen Winter on the phone. I was sure I had phoned her to arrange the meeting in London. I must have phoned the number on the leaflet.

I was beginning to get worried. I phoned a friend of mine, Albert Wilson. Albert was a jeweller too. He had been a jeweller for many years. Albert had taught me all about jewellery-making. I asked Albert about Karen Winter.

'I don't know anyone called Winter,' Albert told me. 'Who does she work for?'

'De Wolf Diamonds,' I said. 'It's a company in Amsterdam.'

'Sorry, James,' Albert said. 'I can't help you. De Wolf Diamonds must be a small company. I don't know them. Are you interested in buying diamonds then?'

'Well,' I explained, 'actually I'm in trouble. I bought some best quality diamonds for an important customer. But I was robbed. The diamonds have been stolen. Now I need to buy some more. I was thinking of buying them from Karen Winter at de Wolf Diamonds. But I can't contact her.'

'I always buy the best quality diamonds from BKV

Diamonds,' said Albert. 'They're a very good company. Why don't you contact them? They're in Amsterdam. You should speak to Mr de Wit. He's the boss.'

'Thanks, Albert,' I said. 'I'll do that.'

There was nothing I could do now. I worked until lunch time. Then I put my things away and went back to Susan's flat. When I arrived, Susan had some bad news for me.

8

'I Must Go to Holland'

I don't know who Karen Winter is,' Susan said. 'But there isn't a company called de Wolf Diamonds.'

'What?' I said. 'How do you know?'

'It was easy to find out,' Susan said. 'I phoned the Chamber of Commerce[36] in Amsterdam. The people there were very helpful. They keep a record of all the companies in Amsterdam. I asked for the phone number of de Wolf Diamonds. I thought perhaps you had written down the wrong number. I wanted to check the number. The people at the Chamber of Commerce checked their computer records carefully. There is no phone number for a diamond company called de Wolf. The company isn't registered. De Wolf Diamonds doesn't exist!

'But if de Wolf Diamonds doesn't exist,' Susan went on, 'who is Karen Winter and who is she working for? Why was she selling you diamonds?'

'It looks like I'm in serious trouble, doesn't it?' I said.

'Yes, it does, James,' Susan said. 'I thought it was strange when you paid twenty thousand pounds in cash. You said it was better to pay in cash. Well, it was certainly better for Karen Winter, wasn't it? The diamonds which you bought were probably stolen. Winter took twenty thousand pounds from you in cash. Then she disappeared. Then the diamonds were stolen again, from you. How can we find Winter now? It's impossible. What a mess!'

'I can't believe it,' I said. 'What about the phone number on the leaflet?'

'What about it?'

'It must be the right number,' I said. 'I'm sure I phoned Karen Winter. I phoned to arrange the meeting in London. I remember that. The phone number that we have must be the right one.'

'James, your memory is bad,' Susan said. 'In London you thought you remembered Karen Winter. You described her. But your description was completely wrong.'

'But I'm sure I'm right this time, Susan,' I said. 'I'm really sure.'

'OK,' Susan said. 'Let's try phoning the number again.'

We phoned the number again. There was no answer. Now I didn't know what to do.

Susan had made sandwiches. We sat at the living room table near the open window. We ate our sandwiches in silence.

I felt puzzled and angry. I stood up and walked around the room. 'I can't understand it!' I said again and again.

I picked up the phone and rang Winter's number again. The phone rang for a long time. No one answered it.

'It must be the wrong number,' said Susan. 'We'll never find Karen Winter.'

The phone continued to ring. Suddenly, the ringing stopped. Someone had answered the phone. A woman spoke in Dutch.

I spoke in English. 'Karen Winter? Hello, this is James

Keating.'

There was silence. Then the woman answered. 'I'm sorry. You have the wrong number,' she said. 'There is no Karen Winter here.'

'Is that Amsterdam 674863?' I said.

'Yes, that's the number,' the woman replied. 'But Karen Winter does not live here.'

'Isn't it the number of de Wolf Diamonds?' I asked.

'No,' she said. 'This is a private flat, not an office.'

'But Karen Winter gave me this number,' I said. 'I spoke to her more than once.'

'I'm sorry, it's impossible,' the woman said. 'There is no one living here now. Mrs van Mander, the owner of the flat, is in hospital. I'm her neighbour. I came in to get some things for Mrs van Mander.'

I couldn't believe it. 'Can you tell me the address please?'

There was silence for a few seconds. 'I'm sorry, you've got the wrong number. There is no Karen Winter here. I can't help you any more.' The woman put the phone down.

Susan and I looked at each other. 'Now we know,' Susan said. 'Winter gave you a false[37] phone number.'

'I must to go to Holland, Susan,' I said. 'I want to speak to Mrs van Mander. She must know something.'

'Are you mad?' Susan said. 'You'll never find Karen Winter. The best thing to do is go to the police. Tell them everything that has happened. There is nothing we can do to find Karen Winter.'

51

'No, Susan,' I said. 'I don't want to go to the police yet. De Wolf Diamonds may be a new company. Perhaps the Chamber of Commerce in Amsterdam doesn't know about it yet. Perhaps the company isn't in Amsterdam. We could look stupid if we went to the police now.' I stopped for a moment. Then I went on, 'There's another reason for going to Holland. I need to buy some quality diamonds for Harvey Chapman. Albert Wilson told me the name of a good company in Amsterdam. We can go there. I'll buy some diamonds and we can go and see Mrs van Mander.'

'But how will you search for Mrs van Mander?' Susan asked. 'How can we find her? We don't know her address.'

'We know her name. We also know her phone number,' I explained. 'We'll look in the Amsterdam phone book. The address will be there next to the number. We'll find her house. Then we can find the neighbour I spoke to on the phone. We must get her to tell us which hospital Mrs van Mander is in.'

We phoned a travel company immediately. There was a plane leaving Birmingham for Amsterdam at 8.30 in the evening. We booked two tickets. It was now 2.30. There was plenty of time. Susan went into town to collect the plane tickets. I went to see my bank manager.

She agreed to lend me the money I needed. Then I went back to my workshop. I did as much work as I could. At five o'clock I went home and packed my suitcase. At 6.30 Susan arrived at my house in her car. She left the car at my house and we took a taxi together to the airport. An hour later we were on the plane, travelling towards Amsterdam.

9

The Search for Mrs van Mander

At Amsterdam airport there was a tourist information office. At this office, we booked rooms in a hotel in the city. Before leaving the airport, we looked for Mrs van Mander's name in the Amsterdam phone book. There were a lot of people called van Mander. But we knew Mrs van Mander's phone number. We soon found the right address. I wrote the address down on a piece of paper. I put the paper inside my wallet.

Our hotel was near the centre of the city. It was in a street beside a canal[38]. There were trees on both sides of the street. The evening air was warm. People were walking along the street looking at the boats on the canal.

The hotel was in an old building. It was narrow and tall. Next door to the hotel there was a restaurant. People were sitting at tables on the pavement outside.

We checked into the hotel. Our rooms were small but comfortable. We unpacked our bags then went out again for a walk.

The city streets were busy. There was music playing everywhere. We sat at a table outside a bar, by a canal and ordered some drinks. It was pleasant to sit there.

For a short time we forgot about thieves, diamonds and all our troubles.

Then Susan suddenly looked worried.

'What's the matter?' I said. 'Are you all right?'

'It's nothing,' Susan said. 'I'm probably imagining things[39].'

'What do you mean?'

'Well, there are two men,' she said. 'They're standing near the canal over there. I think they're watching us.'

I turned and looked towards the canal. There were a lot of people standing there. But I could see two rough-looking men. They were tall and strong. One of the men had tattoos[40] on his arms. He had long, curly, blond hair. The other man had dark hair. He wore a baseball cap. They were looking at us.

'Don't worry Susan,' I said. 'They look rough. But why should they be interested in us?'

'Yes. There's no reason for them to be interested in us,' Susan said.

We finished our drinks and walked back to the hotel. There were still a lot of people in the streets. Our hotel was in a quieter area. We turned off the main street. As we turned, I looked back. About ten metres behind us, I saw the two rough men from the bar. They were following us.

I told Susan to walk faster. She didn't ask questions. She understood the reason why I said this. Now we were in a dark, quiet street. We crossed a bridge over a canal. A boat went slowly past below us. I looked back once more. The two men were still behind us.

We turned another street corner and ran. I could hear the men behind us. They were running too. At the end of the street we turned left into a street with a canal beside it.

'There are two men,' Susan said. 'They're standing near the canal over there. I think they're watching us.'

Our hotel was about thirty metres further on. There were more people in this street. We felt safer. We began to walk again. Soon we were at the hotel.

We collected our room keys from the reception desk and went upstairs. On the first floor there was a window that looked down onto the street below. The two rough–looking men were standing under a tree near the canal. They stood looking at the hotel for a few minutes. Then Susan and I saw them walk slowly away. Why had the two men followed us? What did they want? We couldn't understand.

Next morning, we met early for breakfast. Neither of us had slept well that night. We didn't feel safe. We thought we would see the two men outside the hotel. But they weren't there.

After breakfast, I phoned Mr de Wit at BKV Diamonds. I told him I wanted to buy some best quality diamonds.

'I'll be very happy to do business with a friend of Albert Wilson,' Mr de Wit said to me. 'Come and see me at 2.30 this afternoon.'

'Thank you,' I replied. 'And can I ask you something else?'

'Yes of course,' said Mr de Wit.

'Someone has asked me to contact a company called de Wolf Diamonds. Have you heard of it?'

'De Wolf? No I'm sorry,' said Mr de Wit. 'I don't know any diamond company with that name. I know all the diamond dealers in the city.'

'Oh,' I replied. 'Perhaps my friend has made a mistake.

Thank you very much. I'll see you at 2.30 this afternoon.'

Now we wanted to visit Mrs van Mander. She didn't live in the centre of the city. We went to her home by bus.

Mrs van Mander lived in a large block of flats. The block had eight floors. There were two flats on each floor.

We went inside the building and looked at the names on the doors. Mrs van Mander's flat was on the ground floor.

We knew the flat was empty. We knew that Mrs van Mander was in hospital. But we rang the bell, just to make sure no one was in the flat. Suddenly, the door of the flat opposite opened. A woman came out. She looked about thirty years old. She held a small child in her arms.

'I'm James Keating,' I said. 'I'm looking for Mrs van Mander.'

'She's not at home,' the woman said.

'You're Mrs van Mander's neighbour,' I said. 'I think we spoke on the phone yesterday.'

The woman nodded. 'Yes, I remember,' she said.

'Please can we talk for a moment?' I said. 'It's very important.'

The woman looked worried. After a moment, she said, 'OK, you can come in.'

We followed her into her flat. It was very untidy. Children's toys lay on the floor. We sat down in the living room. The woman put her child on the floor.

'What do you want to talk about?' she asked.

'I'm trying to find a woman called Karen Winter,' I said. 'I think Mrs van Mander can help me. I need to

57

speak to her.'

'Mrs van Mander is very ill,' the neighbour said. 'She's in hospital.'

'How long have you known Mrs van Mander?' I asked.

'I've known her since I moved here, about two years ago,' she said. 'About three months ago, Mrs van Mander became ill. She's seventy-six, you know. She went to stay with her daughter.'

'So Mrs van Mander hasn't lived in the flat for about three months?' Susan said.

'That's right,' the woman replied. 'Then two weeks ago she was seriously ill. She had to go to hospital. She's still in hospital. I visit her when I can.'

Mrs van Mander's flat had been empty for three months. But someone had been in the flat. I knew that. Karen Winter had been there. I had spoken to her on the phone. But how was it possible?

'Has anyone been in Mrs van Mander's flat?' I asked.

'Only me,' she said, 'and Mrs van Mander's daughter who comes here sometimes. She makes sure the flat is all right.'

'Tell me about the daughter,' I said.

'I don't know her well,' the woman said. 'She's about forty years old. She's always well-dressed. I see her when I visit Mrs van Mander in hospital. She goes to the hospital every evening.'

'Has she got dark hair?' asked Susan.

'Yes,' the woman said. 'She's got short, dark hair.'

Susan and I looked at each other. We had the same

idea. Could Karen Winter be Mrs van Mander's daughter?

'Where does Mrs van Mander's daughter live?' I asked.

'I don't know,' the woman said. 'She's got a big flat in the centre of Amsterdam, I think.'

'Do you know where she works?' asked Susan.

The woman shook her head. 'No. Mrs van Mander once told me that her daughter had a good job. That's all I know.'

We were getting close to finding Karen Winter. We had to speak to Mrs van Mander now. 'Which hospital is Mrs van Mander in?' I asked.

The woman wrote down the name and address of the hospital on a piece of paper and gave it to us. We thanked her for her help. Then she picked up her child again, opened the front door and said goodbye.

10

The Attack by the Canal

We went straight to the hospital. The hospital building was enormous. At the information desk, we asked about Mrs van Mander. We found out she was on the fourth floor. We went up to the fourth floor in the lift. A nurse told us where to find Mrs van Mander's bed.

'Mrs van Mander is very ill,' the nurse explained. 'Please don't stay with her very long.'

'We just want to ask her some questions,' I said.

The nurse looked at me. 'Oh, you can't ask her any questions,' she said. 'Mrs van Mander had a serious stroke[41] yesterday. Her brain is damaged. She can't speak at all.'

The nurse pointed to a tiny old lady. The old lady was lying in bed, looking up at the ceiling. I suddenly felt very sad. There was nothing we could do here.

We left the hospital and went into a park that was nearby. We walked through the park and talked about what to do next. It was probable that Karen Winter was Mrs van Mander's daughter. I had to find out. I still couldn't remember anything about my meeting with Karen Winter.

Mrs van Mander's daughter visited her in hospital every evening. We decided to go back to the hospital that evening. I had to meet Mrs van Mander's daughter. If Mrs van Mander's daughter was Karen Winter, perhaps I would recognize her and my memory would return.

60

I had made an appointment to see Mr de Wit at BKV Diamonds. Susan and I looked at our map of the city. BKV Diamonds wasn't far away. The company had its offices near the docks[42] on the River Ij. We decided to walk there.

The diamond company's offices were in a modern building. Next to the offices were some iron gates. The gates led into a courtyard. Blue delivery vans[43] were parked there.

It was lunch time now and we were hungry. My appointment with Mr de Wit wasn't until 2.30. Opposite the diamond company's offices, there was a café. We sat down at a table and ordered lunch.

As we were eating, we talked about Karen Winter.

'If Karen Winter is Mrs van Mander's daughter,' Susan said, 'I don't think she's a diamond dealer. I think she's a crook.'

'Yes, she's probably working with a gang of diamond thieves,' I said. 'They steal the diamonds. Winter sells the diamonds. She is using her mother's empty flat to make phone calls. She arranges meetings with customers on her mother's phone. I thought that phone number was Karen Winter's office number.'

'Of course,' said Susan. 'You met Karen Winter at the Amsterdam Jewellery Trade Fair. She must have asked you to phone her at a certain time when she was at the flat. You must have phoned her and made an appointment to meet her in London to buy the diamonds. After meeting you in London, Winter went back to Holland. She and the diamond thieves were safe. Nobody else knew about the sale. You couldn't find Winter again. Anyway, you wouldn't need to contact her. You had the diamonds and she had the money. It was a very clever arrangement. It was a good way to sell valuable stolen diamonds.'

'Yes. But the diamonds were stolen again,' I said. 'I was robbed on the train coming back from London. Of course, Winter didn't know that would happen. I was unlucky to be attacked on the train. It was unlucky for Winter too, because after the attack I started to look for her. And now we're close to finding her.'

We finished our lunch and ordered coffee. I looked across the street at the offices of BKV Diamonds. A blue delivery van stopped outside the iron gates. The driver got out. He was tall and strong. He had long, curly, blond hair. I recognized him immediately. He was one of the men who had followed us last night. The other man, the one with the baseball cap, was sitting in the passenger seat of the van. We watched the blond-haired man open the gates and then drive the van into the courtyard. A minute later, the two men came out again. They started to cross the road. They were coming towards the café!

'What shall we do?' I said to Susan. 'They're probably coming for lunch. But we don't want them to see us.'

'Right,' said Susan. 'Let's pay the bill and go. Come on. Quick!'

We called the waitress and paid her. We stood up to go. There was no time to drink our coffee. The two rough-looking men were close to the café. We walked away quickly. But the men had seen us.

We went on walking down the street. I looked back. The men were following us. We turned down a side street. There was nobody in this street. We were near the docks. There were warehouses[44] on each side of the street, but no shops or houses.

Suddenly, one of the men ran towards us. We ran too. But there was nowhere to go. The street ended at a canal. In front of us there was water. Behind us the men came running.

We stopped and turned. 'Get ready,' Susan said. 'We'll have to fight.'

The two men ran at us. Susan moved quickly out of the way. I kicked the blond-haired man in the stomach. He groaned[45] and fell to the ground. Then the other man hit me in the face. He grabbed my neck. He was trying to strangle me. I couldn't breathe. The blond-haired man got up. But Susan held him. They struggled. The man was strong. But Susan was a judo champion. She threw him and he landed heavily on the ground.

The man with the baseball cap was strangling me. I couldn't do anything. Susan kicked the man in the back. He let go of my neck and I could breathe again. Susan threw him to the ground. He lay there, groaning in pain.

The blond one had stood up again. He took out a knife. Susan ran at him. She kicked the knife out of his hand. The knife landed on the ground then fell into the water.

Now the man with the baseball cap stood up. We got ready to fight again. But the two men turned and ran away.

Susan ran at him. She kicked the knife out of his hand.

Susan and I were not hurt. I had to thank Susan for that. She had saved us from the two thugs[46]. But why had they attacked us?

I hadn't recognized the two men last night. Now I thought that I had seen them somewhere before. But I couldn't remember where. Anyway, one thing was clear. They knew us. And they didn't want us in Amsterdam.

Susan and I began to walk back down the street. We tried to understand who the thugs were. Why didn't they want us in Amsterdam? Then an idea came to me.

'Those two thugs work for BKV Diamonds,' I said. 'They're delivery drivers. They must be able to get into the company's stockroom[47]. They must be part of the gang of diamond thieves. I think the diamonds I bought in London were stolen from the stockroom at BKV Diamonds. That's why those two thugs don't want us here.'

'But you didn't meet those men when you bought the diamonds,' Susan said. 'It was Karen Winter who sold you the diamonds. How did the thugs recognize you?'

'I'm sure I've seen those two men before, Susan,' I said. 'Perhaps I saw them at the Amsterdam Jewellery Trade Fair. Perhaps they were with Winter then. I don't know. Anyway, they recognized me. They must have seen me somewhere.'

'OK,' Susan said. 'If you're right, what do we do now? Shouldn't we go to the police?'

'Look, it's almost 2.30,' I said. 'Let's go straight to BKV Diamonds and speak to Mr de Wit. The thugs can't hurt us there. We can phone the police from Mr de Wit's office.'

11

We Find Karen Winter

Mr de Wit of BKV Diamonds was short and heavy. He looked about fifty years old and had grey hair. His suit was dark and looked very expensive.

'Mr de Wit, I have something very important to tell you,' I said, after we had introduced ourselves.

'And what is that?' Mr de Wit asked.

'I know who the diamond thieves are,' I said, smiling.

There was a short silence. Mr de Wit looked puzzled. 'I'm sorry, Mr Keating,' he said. 'I don't understand.'

'Haven't you had a robbery here?' I asked. 'Haven't some of your best quality diamonds been stolen?'

Mr de Wit shook his head. 'No,' he said politely.

'Your stockrooms and safes are checked every day, are they?'

'Yes, of course,' Mr de Wit said. 'No diamonds have been stolen.'

'I'm sorry, Mr de Wit,' I said. 'You are wrong. Some valuable diamonds have been stolen.'

'I don't understand.'

'Let me explain,' I said. 'Two days ago, I bought some best quality diamonds in London. The woman who sold them to me was Dutch. I now know that this woman wasn't a diamond dealer. She was a crook. She sold me stolen diamonds. I can tell you where those diamonds came from. They came from your stockrooms, Mr de Wit.

66

The diamonds were stolen by your delivery drivers. I think they saw me in Amsterdam when I first met the woman who sold me the diamonds.'

Mr de Wit was silent for a moment. Then he said, 'So you bought diamonds in London. Please, show them to me. I can tell you if they are mine.'

'I'm afraid I can't show the diamonds to you,' I said. 'The diamonds were stolen from me after I left London. I was robbed on a train near Birmingham.'

'You don't know where the diamonds are now?' Mr de Wit said.

'No, I don't,' I said. 'But I do know that the diamonds are missing from your stockroom. Your delivery drivers stole them.'

'How can you be sure about that?'

'Your delivery drivers saw us in a bar last night,' Susan explained. 'They followed us to our hotel. We didn't know who they were or why they had followed us. Then today, just before coming here, the two delivery drivers saw us again. They followed us and attacked us. We were lucky to get away.'

'There was a fight. But Susan is a judo champion,' I said proudly. 'They didn't expect her to be so strong.'

'My drivers attacked you?! This is very serious,' Mr de Wit said. 'We should report this to the police at once.'

He picked up the phone on his desk and made a phone call. He spoke quickly in Dutch. Then he put the phone down and looked at us. 'The police are coming,' he said. 'You can make a report about the attack when the police arrive.'

'You see, Mr de Wit,' I said, 'the delivery drivers must be the thieves. What other reason could they have for attacking us?'

'I think that we should go to the stockroom now,' Mr de Wit said. 'We'll soon see if any diamonds are missing.'

The stockroom was on the ground floor. It was a large room with a heavy metal door. The stockroom was open. One of Mr de Wit's staff was inside. He was unpacking some boxes.

Mr de Wit spoke to the man. Then Mr de Wit turned to us. 'He says nothing is missing,' he said. 'No diamonds have been stolen, Mr Keating.'

'Is he sure?' I asked.

Mr de Wit opened a metal cupboard. There were drawers inside. He opened the drawers one by one. 'This is where we keep the best quality diamonds,' he said. 'All the diamonds are here. Look, no diamonds have been stolen. Come on, Mr Keating, let's go back to my office.'

I couldn't believe it. I felt stupid and embarrassed[48]. 'I have made a terrible mistake,' I said. 'I'm very sorry.'

Now I didn't know what to think. If the two delivery drivers weren't the diamond thieves, why had they attacked us?

Suddenly there wasn't time to think about this.

From a window, we saw the delivery drivers come into the courtyard outside.

'The drivers are here,' said Mr de Wit. 'I think we should keep them here until the police arrive.'

Then a woman with short, dark hair ran quickly out of the building and into the courtyard. She spoke to the delivery drivers. The woman turned. I could see her face.

'Who's that woman?' I said quickly to Mr de Wit.

'She's one of my staff – she's my Personal Assistant,' Mr de Wit replied.

I recognized her. I remembered who she was. 'Susan, it's her,' I said. 'It's Karen Winter!'

The two thugs jumped into a delivery van. Karen Winter got in after them. The van turned round. At that moment, a police car drove through the gates and into the courtyard. The van's engine roared[49]. The van started to drive away very fast. It hit the back of the police car, but didn't stop. It raced through the gates and away down the street. The police car turned round, raced through the gates too and followed. Its lights were flashing and its siren[50] was wailing loudly.

'What's happening?' said Mr de Wit. 'I don't understand.'

'Mr de Wit, the diamond dealer I met in London, was your Personal Assistant.'

'Who's that woman?' I said quickly to Mr de Wit.

12

I Remember Everything

About twenty minutes later, a police inspector arrived. 'The van has been stopped,' the inspector told us. 'The two men and the woman have been taken to the police station. Now tell me what has been happening.'

'I think Mr Keating should explain,' Mr de Wit said.

I told the inspector everything that I knew. Mr de Wit's Personal Assistant had met me in London at the Chilton Hotel. I knew her as Karen Winter. It was a false name. She sold me some valuable diamonds.

On the train going back to Birmingham, I was attacked and robbed. Karen Winter had tried to make it impossible for me to contact her again. Susan and I came to Amsterdam to look for her.

The two delivery drivers saw us soon after we arrived in Amsterdam. Later, they attacked us. We thought the delivery drivers had stolen the diamonds from BKV's stockroom. But nothing was missing from the stockroom. Finally, Mr de Wit's Personal Assistant and the drivers tried to escape. That was all I knew.

'I want all of you to come down to the police station with me,' the police inspector said. 'You can make a full report there.'

We got into the police inspector's car and drove to the police station. Mr de Wit's Personal Assistant and the two delivery men were already at the police station. The police inspector was going to interview[51] them later. There were still many questions that had to be answered. For example, where had Karen Winter got the diamonds from? They hadn't come from the stockroom at BKV Diamonds.

I tried to remember more about that day when I bought the diamonds in London. Seeing Karen Winter's face had helped my memory. I thought that I was very close to understanding the truth now. My memory was becoming clearer. But how had the two delivery men been involved? They had recognized me at the bar last night. So they must have seen me before Susan and I came to Amsterdam.

The inspector's car stopped outside the police station. As we entered the building I saw one of the delivery men. A policeman was taking him into one of the rooms in the police station. I saw the delivery man's face very clearly. I had seen that face before I came to Holland. But where had I seen it?

Mr de Wit, Susan and I had to make our reports to the police. We were interviewed one after another. I was the last one to be interviewed.

I sat down opposite the inspector. There was also a policewoman in the room. I told my story again to the inspector. He was interested in the two delivery men. 'The delivery men recognized you,' he said. 'They must have seen you somewhere before.'

'And I have seen them too,' I said. 'I'm sure I recognize the blond one's face.'

'Can you remember where you saw him?'

'That's the problem,' I said. 'I was attacked on a train near Birmingham. Since then my memory—'

'— Ah, the train!' the inspector said. 'Is it possible that you saw the delivery drivers there?'

'On the train?' I said.

I had never thought of this. It was an interesting idea. I thought for a few seconds. I tried to remember the train journey from London to Birmingham. I remembered sitting on the train. And I remembered sitting on the park bench in Nuneaton. But what had happened before that?

The policewoman was looking at me. She was wearing small gold earrings. The earrings reminded me of something. Then I understood.

'Can you take me to see the delivery drivers now?' I said. 'If I see them, I can tell you if they were on the train.'

'All right,' the inspector said. 'Come with me.'

The delivery drivers were in another room in the police station. They were sitting with their heads down, looking at the floor. They looked up when I came in. I went straight to the blond one. I lifted back his long curly hair. His left ear was injured. At the bottom of his ear there was a long cut. The cut was new and it looked bad.

'Now I'm sure,' I said to the inspector. 'These men attacked me on the train to Birmingham. While they were attacking, I pulled this man's earring from his ear. Look, you can see the cut. Later, I must have put the earring in my pocket. The police in Birmingham will be able to tell you that my story is true. I made a report to them.

At the bottom of his ear there was a long cut.

The police in Birmingham have the earring.'

We went back to the inspector's office and I finished making my report. Later, a car took Mr de Wit, Susan and me back to BKV Diamonds.

'I can't understand what has happened,' Mr de Wit said as we drove away from the police station.

'Let me explain,' I said. 'Everything is clear to me now. Your Personal Assistant met me at a jewellery trade fair in Amsterdam about month ago. She told me she was a diamond dealer and introduced herself as Karen Winter. It was a false name.'

'Yes, her real name is Gertrud van Mander,' said Mr de Wit.

'Well,' I went on, 'she and the two delivery drivers were working together. On the evening of Friday, 3rd June some quality diamonds were taken from the stockroom at BKV Diamonds. Gertrud van Mander and the two drivers took a plane to London on the Sunday. The next day, I met Gertrud van Mander at the Chilton Hotel. I paid her twenty thousand pounds in cash for the diamonds.

'When I left the hotel, the drivers followed me. Their plan was to steal the diamonds back again. On the train, they attacked me. They got the diamonds and pushed me from the train. They returned to Holland immediately. Monday, 6th June was a holiday in Holland. Early on the Tuesday morning, the diamonds were put back in the stockroom at BKV Diamonds. Nobody knew that the diamonds had been missing!'

Mr de Wit was shocked. 'I don't believe this!' he said. 'I

have known Gertrud van Mander for many years. She has always worked very hard and I've trusted her. And all this time she's been cheating me! She has been using my diamonds to steal money from people.'

The police car stopped outside the offices of BKV Diamonds and we got out. When we were inside the building, Mr de Wit spoke to one of his staff. Then he turned to Susan and me.

'Please come with me,' he said. 'Let's sit down and have some coffee. We've all had a great shock.'

We followed Mr de Wit to his office. Coffee was brought in. As we were drinking our coffee, the phone rang. Mr de Wit picked up the phone and spoke in Dutch. After a few minutes, he put the phone down.

'That was the police inspector,' he said. 'He has interviewed the drivers and Gertrud van Mander. They have admitted[52] everything. You were right, Mr Keating. They did steal the diamonds.' Mr de Wit was silent for a moment. Then he said, 'I am very sorry for what has happened to you.'

'And I am sorry for you,' I replied. 'We have both been robbed and cheated.'

There was a knock on the door and one of the staff came in. He was carrying some large, flat boxes. He put the boxes on Mr de Wit's desk, then left the office.

'We still have some business to discuss, I think,' Mr de Wit said. 'You came here to buy diamonds.' He opened the flat boxes. They were full of beautiful diamonds. Mr de Wit switched on the light on his desk. 'I hope you can find what you want,' he said.

I chose the diamonds I needed for Harvey Chapman's brooch. Then I looked for two more diamonds for the ring. The ring! Who had asked me to make it? I had remembered everything else now. I was annoyed that I couldn't remember who the ring was for. I had the design of the ring with me. I put it on the desk and I looked at it carefully. I picked up a couple of diamonds and looked at each one under the light. They glittered and shone. They were pure, transparent diamonds. I looked at the diamonds and at my design. They were perfect.

I looked up and smiled. At last I had remembered everything. My memory had returned.

'Is anything wrong?' asked Susan.

'No, nothing's wrong,' I said. 'These diamonds are excellent. They're just what I'm looking for.'

Later that evening, Susan and I flew back to Birmingham. We both felt tired but very happy. The mystery had been solved. My memory had returned. But I still had one small problem. Harvey Chapman wanted the diamond ring for Pauline Greenwood, the film star. But I couldn't make the ring for Harvey Chapman now. I had designed the ring for someone else. Harvey Chapman wouldn't be pleased when I told him he couldn't have it. But I had to tell him.

13

The Diamond Ring

We arrived at my house in Sutton Street at midnight. There were a few messages on my answering machine. Two of the messages were from Harvey Chapman. As usual, he was very angry.

It was too late to phone Harvey Chapman now. I phoned him early the next morning.

'Where have you been, Keating?' he asked angrily. 'I've been trying to speak to you.'

'I've been away, Mr Chapman,' I said.

'You're never here when I want you, Keating,' Chapman said. 'What about my jewellery? Have you finished it?'

'Finished?' I said. 'I've only just started making it. You know that.'

'Listen, Keating,' Chapman said. 'I have to go back to America sooner than I thought. I'm going next week. I want to take the jewellery with me. You'll have to work fast!'

'You can't have the jewellery by next week,' I said. 'I need more time. And there's another thing I need to tell you. I can't make the ring for you. The ring is for someone else.'

'What?' Chapman shouted. He was very angry. 'I've had enough of your jokes, Keating. I've told you before. I don't like you. I don't like the way you do business. Now if you don't make me that ring, I won't buy the brooch. Do you understand? No ring, no brooch.'

'I'm sorry, Mr Chapman,' I said. 'I can't sell you the ring. I could design another ring for you.'

'I don't want another ring, Keating!' Chapman shouted. 'I've had enough of you. That's it, the deal is off[53]. You'll never work for me.' He shouted something unpleasant then threw the phone down.

I had lost Harvey Chapman as a customer. I wasn't going to be famous in Hollywood. But I didn't care about that now. I was happy that I didn't have to work for Chapman any more.

For the next few weeks, I worked very hard on the diamond ring. It was a beautiful ring. It was the best piece of jewellery that I had ever made.

I was working late in my workshop one evening, when the phone rang. It was Susan. She was very upset. 'James, you forgot again, didn't you?' she said. 'You were going to come to my flat for dinner at 7.30!'

It was true. I had forgotten. I had been working very hard to finish the ring.

'Don't be angry, Susan,' I said. 'I'm leaving the workshop now. I'll be at your flat in fifteen minutes.'

I put the ring carefully in a box. I put away my tools and went straight to Susan's flat. Susan was still angry. At first she didn't speak to me. The meal was on the table. The hot food had gone cold. Susan was sitting on the couch. Music was playing quietly.

'I'm very sorry I forgot about the dinner, Susan,' I said.

'I forgot because I was doing something important.'

'Doing something more important than having dinner with me?'

I sat down beside Susan. I held her very close and kissed her. 'I'm a very lucky man,' I said. 'I think you're fantastic.' I kissed her again.

Susan was silent for a while. Then at last she smiled. 'You're terrible!' she said. 'Why do I love you so much?'

I took out a little box from my pocket. I gave the box to Susan.

'I forgot about dinner because I was finishing something,' I said. 'Go on, open the box!'

Susan lifted the lid of the box. Her eyes opened wide. There was a big smile on her face. She picked up the diamond ring and held it between her fingers. The diamonds glittered and shone in the light.

'Oh, it's wonderful, James,' Susan said. 'I've never seen such a beautiful ring.' She held me close to her and kissed me. 'Thank you very much.'

'I always knew that the ring was special,' I said. 'And finally I remembered why the ring was special. I had designed it for a very special person – for the woman I love. I could never have sold it to Harvey Chapman.'

Susan picked up the diamond ring and
held it between her fingers.

POINTS
FOR
UNDERSTANDING

Points for Understanding

1

1 Where is the person who is telling the story?
2 Who does this person meet?
3 What does the person find in their pockets?
4 What is the person's name and where do they live?

2

1 Why couldn't James understand how he had arrived in Nuneaton?
2 Who has left messages on his answering machine?
3 Suddenly the door opened and someone came in. What happens next?
4 What does Susan tell James about himself?
5 Where does Susan think the earring came from?
6 Who is Harvey Chapman?

3

1 Where do Susan and James go before they go to his workshop?
2 Why does Susan become angry with James?
3 James finds two unusual jewellery designs in his workshop. What are the designs for?
4 What arrangement does James make with Harvey Chapman?
5 James' bank manager tells James what he did yesterday. What was this?
6 Where does James decide to go?

4

1 'You really have been very stupid. James,' says Susan. Why does she say this?

2 What does Martin Sanders tell James about his visit to London the day before?

5

1 Who had James met at the Chilton Hotel?
2 What information does the receptionist have about this person?
3 Why does James want to find this person?
4 What does this person look like?
5 Why do Susan and James decide to look through the leaflets and brochures in his office?
6 What piece of information does the ticket inspector give James? Why is it useful?

6

1 Why is Harvey Chapman angry with James again?
2 Describe Harvey Chapman and his house.
3 James and Harvey Chapman have a disagreement about the design for a ring. Why?

7

1 What has Susan found in James' office?
2 Perhaps I had written the number down incorrectly. Why does James think this?
3 What does Albert Wilson tell James?

8

1 What has Susan found out about de Wolf Diamonds?
2 James phones Holland. Who does he speak to? What information does she give him?
3 Why does James decide to go to Amsterdam?

9

1 How do James and Susan find Mrs van Mander's address?
2 Describe the two men that James and Susan see in the bar.
3 Neither of us had slept well that night. What had happened that evening? Why had James and Susan been frightened?
4 What do James and Susan learn from Mrs van Mander's neighbour?

10

1 Why can't James and Susan talk to Mrs van Mander?
2 Why do they decide to go back to the hospital that evening?
3 James makes an appointment for 2.30. Where is the appointment and who is it with?
4 'It was a very clever arrangement,' says Susan. What is Susan talking about?
5 Why do James and Susan have to run away from the café?
6 Why does James decide that the two thugs must be the diamond thieves?

11

1 'I don't understand,' says Mr de Wit.
   What has James told him?
2 Why does Mr de Wit decide to phone the police?
3 What do James, Susan and Mr de Wit find out when they go to the stockroom?
4 What happens as the police arrive?

12

1 Why do the police take James, Susan and Mr de Wit to the police station?
2 Who has also been taken to the police station?

3 James asks if he can see the delivery drivers.
   (a)   What does James do when he sees them?
   (b)   What does he find out?
   (c)   What does this tell him?
4 What is Karen Winter's real name?
5 What has she been doing with Mr de Wit's diamonds?
6 What does James do before he leaves BKV Diamonds?
7 James still had 'one small problem'. What was his problem?

13

1 What does Chapman want James to do?
2 'No ring, no brooch,' says Chapman.
   Why does he say this? What does he mean?
3 James forgets to go to Susan's flat at 7.30. How does she feel?
4 Why had James forgotten to go to Susan's flat?

GLOSSARY

Glossary

1 **torn** – *to be torn* (page 7)
large holes have been made in the cloth by someone pulling roughly at the jacket.

2 **attack** – *to be attacked* (page 7)
hurt by someone who suddenly hits you.

3 **aspirin** (page 7)
medicine you take to stop a pain or a fever. Aspirins are usually pills that you swallow with water.

4 **report** – *to report the attack to the police* (page 7)
go to the police and tell them what happened. A police-officer writes down what you say. When your report has been written down you sign your name on it.

5 **return ticket** (page 8)
a train ticket that allows you to travel from one place to another and come back again.

6 **answering machine** (page 9)
a machine that is fixed to a phone. It records your phone messages for you while you are away.

7 **main railway line** (page 10)
one of the most important routes on a railway. Main railway lines go between cities and large towns. Small towns are often on less important routes – *branch* lines.

8 **excuse** (page 11)
what you say to someone to tell them why you could not do something. Harvey Chapman is saying that James must have a very good reason for not meeting him.

9 **burglars** (page 11)
thieves who get into peoples' houses to steal things.

10 **grab** – *to grab someone* (page 11)
hold someone quickly and roughly.

11 **couch** (page 12)
a long, comfortable seat for two or more people.

12 **teacher of physical education and a judo champion** (page 14)
someone who teaches sport is a physical education teacher. A judo champion is someone who has won competitions in ju-jitsu – a kind of Japanese fighting.

13 **connected with** – *to be connected with* (page 15)
   have something to do with.
14 **tidy** – *to be tidy* (page 18)
   put things away carefully. James is *untidy*. He does not remember
   to put his papers away in drawers or to keep his office clean.
15 **inexpensive** (page 20)
   something which does not cost much money to make or to buy.
16 **brooch** (page 20)
   a pretty pin that is fastened on to clothes. Brooches are often
   made of gold, silver or jewels.
17 **pure and transparent** (page 21)
   pure means there are no marks in the diamonds. Transparent
   means that the diamonds are clear and light shines brightly
   through them. Pure and transparent diamonds are of very good
   quality and are very valuable.
18 **I'm tired of this** (page 21)
   a way of saying you are angry about something that has happened
   many times.
19 **bank clerk** (page 22)
   a person who works in a bank. Bank clerks meet the customers
   who want to pay money into a bank or take money out. Customers
   keep their money in *bank accounts* in banks. If someone wants to
   buy something, but they don't have enough money in their
   account, the bank can lend them some money. They will have to
   pay this money (a loan) back to the bank later. A *bank manager* is
   the person in charge of the *branch* – or office – of a bank. Many
   banks have branches in different towns or cities.
20 **in cash** – *pay for something in cash* (page 25)
   pay for something with bank notes or coins.
21 **by cheque** – *pay for something by cheque* (page 25)
   pay for something by writing a cheque. The customer writes the
   seller's name on the cheque. The customer has to write how
   much the goods are and sign the cheque. The seller then takes
   the cheque to their own bank. The seller's bank will then get the
   money from the customer's bank account.
      Cheques are safer to carry than cash. A thief can only use
   someone's cheques if they can copy that person's signature exactly.
22 **diamond dealer** (page 25)
   someone who buys and sells diamonds.

23 **deal** – *to get a better deal* (page 25)
a deal is an agreement to buy or sell something. If you pay for
something with cash you can sometimes pay less. This is because
the seller might have to pay some of the money to a bank if the
customer pays by cheque.

24 *your own fault* (page 26)
bad things have happened to James because of what he has done.

25 **booked** – *to book* (page 31)
made an arrangement to stay in the hotel.

26 *probably* (page 32)
very possibly.

27 *jewellery trade fair* (page 34)
a place where people who buy, sell or make jewellery meet.

28 *sharp bend* (page 34)
a place on the railway line where the track goes suddenly to the
right or left.

29 *express trains* (page 35)
fast trains that go from one city to another city without stopping
at the smaller towns.

30 *well-organized* – *to be well-organized* (page 37)
thinks about things carefully and does them well.

31 *let's get this clear* (page 39)
let's both understand what is happening.

32 *puzzled* – *to look puzzled* (page 40)
not understanding something, so your face shows you are
confused or worried. A *puzzle* is a mystery or a problem you don't
understand.

33 *arrange a loan* (page 45)
ask a bank to lend you money (see Glossary No. 19).

34 *orders* (page 45)
a list of information about jobs for customers.

35 *safe* (page 46)
a box or cupboard made of thick metal with a strong lock.
Valuable things are kept in safes.

36 **Chamber of Commerce** (page 49)
an organization that helps people in business.

37 *false* (page 51)
not correct. Karen Winter has given James someone else's phone
number.

38 **canal** (page 53)
    a channel that has been cut in the ground. It is full of water so
    boats can travel along it.
39 **imagining things** – to imagine things (page 54)
    thinking that you can see something but you are not sure.
40 **tattoos** (page 54)
    pictures made on someone's skin with a needle and ink.
41 **stroke** (page 60)
    a sudden illness of the brain. Often, people who have strokes
    cannot see, hear, walk or talk afterwards.
42 **docks** (page 61)
    places where ships stop. Ships can be repaired in docks.
    Passengers can get on or off ships in docks. Or goods can be taken
    off the ships, or put onto them.
43 **delivery vans** (page 61)
    vehicles that a company use to carry goods or to deliver goods to
    customers.
44 **warehouses** (page 63)
    large buildings where goods are kept.
45 **groaned** – to groan (page 63)
    made a noise because he felt pain.
46 **thugs** (page 65)
    rough, dangerous robbers.
47 **stockroom** (page 65)
    a large room where goods are kept.
48 **embarrassed** – to be embarrassed (page 68)
    felt uncomfortable because he had done something foolish.
49 **roared** – to roar (page 69)
    the engine made a loud noise because the van is about to drive
    away very fast.
50 **siren** (page 69)
    the thing on a police car that makes a loud noise.
51 **interview** – to interview (page 72)
    ask questions to find out the truth.
52 **admitted** – to admit everything (page 76)
    told the truth and said they have done something wrong.
53 **deal is off** (page 79)
    a way of saying that you no longer want to buy or sell something.

Oliver Twist *by Charles Dickens*
The Bonetti Inheritance *by Richard Prescott*
No Comebacks *by Frederick Forsyth*
The Enchanted April *by Elizabeth Von Arnim*
The Three Strangers *by Thomas Hardy*
The Pearl *by John Steinbeck*
The Woman Who Disappeared *by Philip Prowse*
A Town Like Alice *by Nevil Shute*
The Queen of Death *by John Milne*
Meet Me in Istanbul *by Richard Chisholm*
The Great Gatsby *by F. Scott Fitzgerald*
The Space Invaders *by Geoffrey Matthews*
My Cousin Rachel *by Daphne du Maurier*
I'm the King of the Castle *by Susan Hill*
Dracula *by Bram Stoker*
The Sign of Four *by Sir Arthur Conan Doyle*
The Speckled Band and Other Stories by *Sir Arthur Conan Doyle*
The Queen of Spades and Other Stories *by Aleksandr Pushkin*
The Diamond Hunters *by Wilbur Smith*
When Rain Clouds Gather *by Bessie Head*
Banker *by Dick Francis*
No Longer at Ease *by Chinua Achebe*
The Franchise Affair *by Josephine Tey*
The Case of the Lonely Lady *by John Milne*
Silas Marner *by George Eliot*
Pride and Prejudice *by Jane Austen*
Wuthering Heights *by Emily Brontë*
Jurassic Park *by Michael Crichton*

For further information on the full selection of
Readers at all five levels in the series, please refer
to the Heinemann Readers catalogue.

Published by Macmillan Heinemann ELT
Between Towns Road, Oxford OX4 3PP
Macmillan Heinemann ELT is an imprint of
Macmillan Publishers Limited
Companies and representatives throughout the world
Heinemann is a registered trademark of Harcourt Education, used under licence.

ISBN 978–1–4050–7304–2

This is a work of fiction. Any similarities to people, institutions,
corporations or public bodies bearing the same name are purely coincidental.

Illustrated by Derek Bishop
Typography by Adrian Hodgkins
Designed by Sue Vaudin
Cover illustration by Oliver Burston

Printed in Thailand

2011 2011 2009 2008 2007
10   9   8   7   6   5   4